SHIRE NATURAL

C000089109

GORS

C. J. HUMPHRIES and E. SHAUGHNESSY

CONTENTS

COVER: *Common Gorse flowering by the shores of Loch Ine, Republic of Ireland*

Series editors: Jim Flegg and Chris Humphries.

Set in 9 point Times roman and printed in Great Britain by C. I. Thomas & Sons (Haverfordwest) Ltd, Press Buildings, Merlins Bridge, Haverfordwest, Dyfed.

Introduction

The Common Gorse *(Ulex europaeus)*, also known as Furze or Whin, is the most widespread of seven extremely spiny shrub species found predominantly in the warmer parts of Spain and Portugal, but with an obvious Atlantic distribution in Europe. Although the three species in the British Isles are regarded by many as mere scrub weeds, gorses are very attractive, biologically interesting and important members of heathland communities. Not only are they dominant species in the ecology of poorer soils and heathland wildlife but they have, especially in the recent past, also played an important role in rural economies and have given rise to a rich rural folklore.

The names 'gorse' and 'furze' are derived from the Anglo-Saxon words *gorst* and *fyrs*. 'Whin' is slightly more obscure but is thought to have originated in Scandinavia, first occurring in Britain in the north. All three terms have been used in various forms and with local variations. Gorse bushes are often referred to as 'gorst bushes', 'furze bushes', 'furzen bushes', or 'whin bushes'. A bundle of gorse twigs is sometimes called a 'gorse-kid'. Animals and especially birds that are associated with gorse often have a local name reflecting this. For example, the Mountain Finch or Brambling *(Fringilla montifringilla)* is also known as the 'furze chucker'. Areas in which gorse is found are often described as 'gorsy', 'furzy', 'fuzzy' or 'whinny'. Gorse has many delightful local names, varying from county to county. Some of the more colourful examples include 'Fingers and Thumbs' (Wiltshire) 'French Fuzz' (Devon, Cornwall and Ireland), 'Furra' (Norfolk), 'Gorst' (Midlands), 'Hawth' and 'Hoth' (Sussex), 'Honey Bottle' (Somerset), 'Ling' (Derbyshire and the north of England), 'Pins and Needles' and 'Thumbs and Fingers' (Somerset), 'Vuzz' (Devon) as well as 'Goss', 'Prickly Broom', 'Ruffet' and 'Frey'.

The Pea Family and *Ulex* species

The genus *Ulex* belongs to the huge Pea Family (Leguminosae or Fabaceae), a group of 12,000 species distributed throughout the world including all the familiar beans, clovers, lupins, rest-harrows and medicks. The family occurs in every type of soil and climate and shows a great variety in habit, including trees, shrubs, water plants, desert plants and climbers. The roots possess peculiar tubercles, which are modified lateral roots that contain bacterial organisms of the genus *Rhizobium* — organisms that are capable of fixing atmospheric nitrogen.

The stems are mostly erect and there are many climbers in the family. Some, such as *Vicia,* have leaves modified into climbing tendrils, whilst others climb by twining. The vegetative parts can become modified in a variety of different ways in the family; thorns are modified branches in *Gleditsia,* stipules in *Acacia* and leaves in *Ulex*. The leaves are mostly alternate, stipulate and compound. *Ulex* is very unusual in having small leaves. Other modifications include phyllodes, which are petioles acting as leaves, as found in acacias, and some leaves are even sensitive to touch as in the Telegraph Plant *(Mimosa pudica)*.

The Leguminosae family is split into three subfamilies: Mimosoideae, Caesalpinioideae and Lotoideae. The seven species of *Ulex* constitute a natural group characterised by spine-like leaves and they are classified, with other shrubby European legumes with fused stamen filaments, into the tribe Genisteae. *Ulex* is most closely allied to the brooms of *Cytisus* and *Stauracanthus*.

The most obvious and striking character of *Ulex* species is the dense, very dark-green spines which thickly cover every branch. There are noticeably few linear leaves and most of the spines are modified leaves. At the seedling stages,

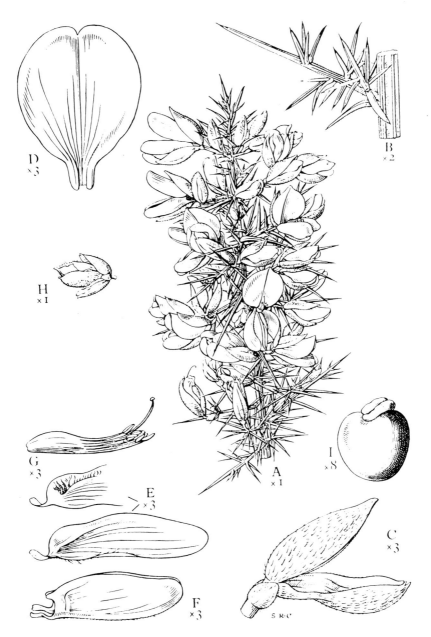

1. *Common Gorse (Ulex europaeus). A, flowering stem; B, part of main stem with branched spine and leaves; C, calyx and bracteoles (note caruncle); D, standard; E, wing, inner surface, and part of outer surface; F, keel; G, stamens and stigma; H, fruit; I, seed. Petals bright golden yellow.*

3

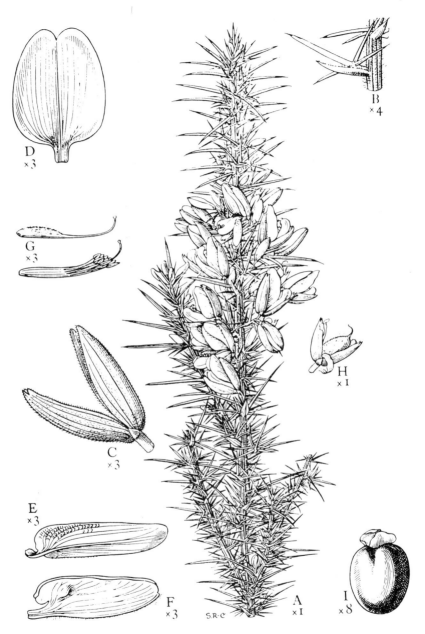

2. *Western Furze (Ulex gallii). A, flowering branch; B, part of stem with spines and leaves; C, calyx and bracteole; D, standard; E, wing, outer surface; F, keel; G, stamens and stigma; H, fruit; I, seed. Petals yellow.*

3. *Flowering shoot of Common Gorse (Ulex europaeus) in mid April.*

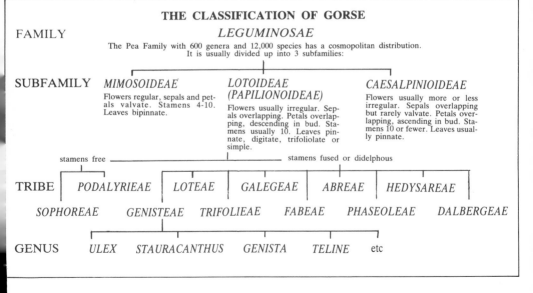

THE CLASSIFICATION OF GORSE

FAMILY — *LEGUMINOSAE*

The Pea Family with 600 genera and 12,000 species has a cosmopolitan distribution. It is usually divided up into 3 subfamilies:

SUBFAMILY

MIMOSOIDEAE
Flowers regular, sepals and petals valvate. Stamens 4-10. Leaves bipinnate.

LOTOIDEAE (PAPILIONOIDEAE)
Flowers usually irregular. Sepals overlapping. Petals overlapping, descending in bud. Stamens usually 10. Leaves pinnate, digitate, trifoliolate or simple.

CAESALPINIOIDEAE
Flowers usually more or less irregular. Sepals overlapping but rarely valvate. Petals overlapping, ascending in bud. Stamens 10 or fewer. Leaves usually pinnate.

stamens free ———————————————— stamens fused or didelphous

TRIBE — *PODALYRIEAE* | *LOTEAE* | *GALEGEAE* | *ABREAE* | *HEDYSAREAE*

SOPHOREAE   *GENISTEAE*   *TRIFOLIEAE*   *FABEAE*   *PHASEOLEAE*   *DALBERGEAE*

GENUS — *ULEX*   *STAURACANTHUS*   *GENISTA*   *TELINE*   etc

in *U. europeaus* (the Common Gorse) for example, the first twelve pairs of leaves are trifoliate (three lobed) like shamrock, a feature common to most members of the Leguminosae. The condition is so extreme in *U. gallii* that only the first pair of leaves is trifoliate. All subsequent leaves are reduced to small scale-like appendages or modified into the characteristic spines that are called phyllodes.

Like all members of the subfamily Lotoideae, the flowers of *Ulex* are noticeably bilaterally symmetrical (zygomorphic) which means that they can be divided into two equal and opposite halves. The petals are bright yellow and occur singly or in clusters inside the calyces at the base of the phyllode axils, at the union of the spines and shoots. As with other legume flowers, when viewed from the front, there are five petals: there is a large standard turning from its centre upwards, two lateral petals called wings and two lower petals joined at their lower margins into a keel. The calyx is also more or less yellow, tube-like but divided to the base into two lips, the upper lip has two teeth, the lower lip three teeth. The ten stamens consist of the pollen-bearing anthers and the filaments fused about halfway down their length into a tube. The style sits inside the stamen tube and sticks out from the front. The pods of all species are broadly ovoid to linear-oblong in shape. They are brown or black and hairy and they hardly emerge from the calyces at maturity. Between one and six seeds occur in each pod.

THE SPECIES

Despite there being a number of fairly modern descriptions of the different gorses, the variation and delimitation of species is still imperfectly understood. This is probably because hybridisation between species is much more frequent than observers suppose and a number of isolated populations, especially in the Iberian peninsula, have been given species names when they are merely segregates of other species. We think that there are seven species altogether: *Ulex europaeus, U. minor, U. gallii, U. densus, U. parviflorus, U. micranthus* and *U. argenteus*. The first three occur in Britain but the remainder occur in mainland Europe. *Ulex europaeus,* the Common Gorse, Furze or Whin, is a dark-green shrub usually about 1.5 metres (5 feet) high but occasionally attaining 2 metres (6 feet) and more rarely up to 5.5 metres (18 feet) in height in very shaded conditions. It is extremely spiny and the main branches are hairy. From the main branches spring numerous short side branches which grow horizontally and always end in a stout, sharp spine; the whole plant forms a dense, entangled, formidable mass. The leaves are up to 2 cm (¾ inch) long, linear and sharply pointed or merely a spine. The spines are furrowed, presumably to reduce water loss in dry conditions. Technically, Common Gorse is recognised by the relatively large oval bracts, which measure about 4 mm (⅛ inch) long by 2 mm (¹⁄₁₆ inch) wide, and by the erect hairs on the calyx.

The flowers may occur singly from the end of September onwards, even during the winter months when the weather is mild. However, Common Gorse comes to full bloom in April. The flowers are produced singly from the leaf axils of the previous year's shoots. In a good season the ends of each branch are densely covered in the brilliant golden flowers — a marvellous sight on large heaths in springtime. The ripe pods are about 2 cm (¾ inch) long and covered in brown hairs.

Ulex gallii, Western Furze, is known as 'Bed Furze' in Hampshire, 'Cat Whin' in Cumbria, 'Cornish Fuzz' or 'Tam-fuzz' in Cornwall and even 'Dwarf Gorse' or 'Summer Gorse' in some areas. It forms stiffer-spined plants than *U. europaeus.* It generally grows as a low shrub, usually less than 1 metre (3 feet) high. The spines are very strong, only slightly furrowed and often curved. Like its cousin *U. minor,* it technically differs from the Common Gorse by the minute bracts which subtend the flowers. Also, the calyx is about 10 mm (⅜ inch) long and the calyx hairs are very adpressed. The flowers are a beautiful deep golden-yellow, staying in full bloom from July to October, or even to November in areas such as Cornwall.

In Britain there have been a few records of hybrids between *Ulex europaeus* and *U. gallii.* However, although

6

4. *Dwarf Furze (Ulex minor). A, part of a flowering plant, and a small piece of fruiting stem; B, apex of stem with leaves and spines; C, calyx and bracteole; D, standard; E, wing, outer surface; F, keel; G, stamens and stigma; H, seed. Petals yellow.*

CHARACTERISTICS OF GORSE SPECIES

Ulex species	*europaeaus*	*minor*	*gallii*	*densus*	*parviflorus*	*micranthus*	*argenteus*
Bracteole width (mm)	2	1.5	1.5	1.5	1.5	1.5	1.5
Primary phyllode length (mm)	8	5	5+	5-8	2-5(-6)	2-3.5	2-4.5
Terminal spine length (mm)	12-25 (30)	8-15	8-15	8-20	4-30	7-12	5-20 (-35)
Terminal spine shape	stout, straight	weak, straight or curved	weak, straight or curved	weak, straight	weak, straight or curved	stout, recurved	stout, straight
Secondary phyllodes: less than half as long as lateral spines (1), more than half as long as lateral spines (2)	2	2	2	2	1	1	1
Hairs on short shoots and spines	somewhat glaucous	somewhat softly hairy at the base	softly hairy at the base	hirsute or villous	glabrous or curly pubescent	glabrous or with curly patent hairs	persistent adpressed hairs
Plant colour	dark green	dark green	dark green	pale green	dark green	dark green	glaucous grey-green
Petal colour	clear yellow	clear yellow	deep golden-yellow	yellow	yellow	yellow	yellow
Petals and calyx, relative length	wings straight, longer than keel, both exceeding calyx	wings and keel equal, about equal to calyx	wings and keel slightly exceeding calyx, by 2.5-3.5 mm	standard and keel equalling calyx, wings 2 mm shorter	standard equalling calyx, wings shorter	petals equal, exceeding calyx	standard equalling calyx, wings shorter

5 (opposite). *Successful colonisation of gorse along the M3 motorway.*

6 (below). *Wind-grazed gorse on rocky cliffs.*

they can be locally common, they are generally rare. They can be recognised by the intermediate thickness of the flower stalks, the shape of the flower bracts and the hairs on the calyx.

Ulex minor, Small Furze or Dwarf Furze, is a small prostrate shrub, usually about 0.3 metre (1 foot) high but up to almost 1 metre (3 feet) high in some parts of Britain. Its spines are weak and very slender and the flower bracts are minute. The flowers are a distinctly paler and purer yellow than its sister species, and they bloom from July to October in most places.

Ulex densus is a very spiny, dense, compact bush up to about 50 cm (20 inches) tall at its maximum. The young twigs, spines and phyllodes are hairy with white or pale brown hairs. This species is somewhat pale green compared with the other species and the phyllodes are softer and more flexible than its close relatives. It grows on dry, calcareous soils in western and central parts of Portugal.

Ulex parviflorus is perhaps the most variable species, especially in southern Spain and Portugal: at one time it was considered to be fifteen separate species. The habit is very variable but it can attain 1.5 metres (5 feet) in height. The most conspicuous identifying characters are the standard and keel of the flowers, which are more or less equal in length to the calyx, whilst the wings are shorter. In all other species the wings are longer than the calyx. The other characters show a confusing array of variability. The spiny shoots can be straight or recurved. They are often, but not always, covered in curly hairs or occasionally with straight white hairs. This species grows throughout south-western Europe from Portugal to the south of France.

Ulex micranthus is a small, rather open bush, usually between 20 and 50 cm (8 to 20 inches) in height. The rather sparingly branched stems are somewhat straight, erect or curving upwards and dark green. The spines are somewhat recurved and very stout. In this species all of the petals are longer than the calyx. It grows on heathlands with acid soils in north-west Portugal and extends into north-west Spain.

Ulex argenteus is characterised by the short shoots being covered in persistent white adpressed hairs, giving it a silvery grey appearance. It is generally a low-growing species found in the oak woods and scrubby areas of the Algarve and south-west Alentejo or on sandy soils near the sea at Faro. There is one locality in Spain, Cabo de Gata, where it grows on rocky headlands.

Pollination and seed development

Flowers which seem to be most closely associated with specific pollinators are invariably those which have a specialised shape. Gorse flowers, like most other members of the Leguminosae family, have the typical bilaterally symmetrical pea-flower shape normally associated with heavy insect pollinators. In the insect-pollinated legumes the five petals form a single unit, firmly interlocking with one another at their bases or margins with pegs or folds. Each legume species differs slightly in its details. In a new gorse flower the two keel petals interlock slightly by their upper edges and the keel is held straight by the stamens and style inside. The lower half of the stamen filaments are fused into a strong tube and the style sits in the middle. *Ulex* species are visited mainly by bumble bees and honey bees. A visiting bee usually clings to the wing petals and inserts its proboscis between the standard petal and the keel in a vain search for nectar, which in other legumes lies inside the stamen tube. The gorse flowers are nectarless but the bees are attracted by the sweet, coconut-scented perfume and by the strong colour, which absorbs ultra-violet light and is therefore very prominent to a bee's eyesight.

The bees forcibly enter the flowers, an action which breaks the keel apart, uncovering the stamens and bringing them

7 (above, left). *A honey-bee forces entry into a fresh flower of Common Gorse.*

8 (above, right). *It searches vainly for nectar while being dusted with pollen.*

9 (right). *The bee leaves the flower, covered in pollen, following the explosion of the stamens.*

to a swift, sharp contact with the bee, dusting pollen on to the underside of the bee's body. Once burst open, the spent petals hang limply down the side of the flower and are rarely, if ever, visited again by a bee. As the bees flit from one flower to another, pollination is effected. Eventually, after fertilisation, which takes place in the spring, the pods develop within the calyx, becoming ripe in July for Common Gorse and in July to September for the two smaller species. On a hot summer's day a gorse heath becomes alive with 'popping' sounds, as each pod dries out. The stresses along the pod margins become too great for the marginal cells to hold them any longer. As the sutures split, the pods twist violently, ejecting the hard, shiny seeds distances of up to 3 metres (10 feet). The seeds are reputedly spread further by ants, which bite and tear at the fleshy, orange *caruncle* (a fleshy appendage for soaking up water), dropping the seeds along the ground as they do so.

Distribution and habitat

Ulex micranthus, U. argenteus and *U. densus* are restricted entirely to heathland in the Iberian peninsula, mostly southern Spain and Portugal. *U. parviflorus* has a western Mediterranean distribution pattern, occurring in the Balearic Islands, southern France, Spain and Portugal. *U. gallii* and *U. minor* have an Atlantic distribution in Europe, *U. gallii* in Britain, France, Ireland and Spain, and *U. minor* in Britain, France, Spain and Portugal. *U. europaeus* is the most widespread species, occurring throughout much of Europe — to Norway and Sweden in the north, Austria and Czechoslovakia in the east and North Africa in the south.

10 (opposite). *Western Furze with Bell Heather (Erica cinerea).*

11 (below). *Western Furze: a close-up of a shoot.*

12. *Distribution of Common Gorse (Ulex europaeus) in the British Isles. The back dots refer to 10 km grid squares in which the species has been recorded. Note its absence from heavily cultivated areas in East Anglia and from northern England and Scotland.*

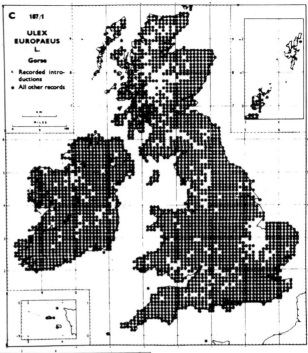

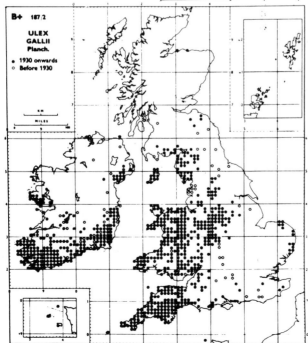

13. *Distribution of Western Gorse (Ulex gallii) in the British Isles. It is predominant in moist western and southern areas of south-west England and Ireland.*

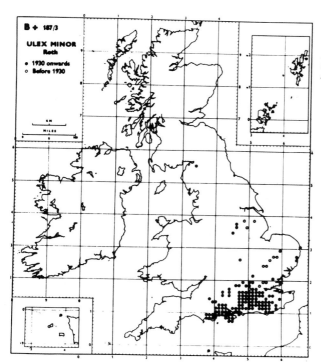

14. *Distribution of Dwarf Furze (Ulex minor) in the British Isles. It is a species of southern dry heaths.*

All species occur predominantly in heathland habitats. Of the British species, *Ulex europaeus* occurs in rough grassy places and heaths, usually in abundance on light, impoverished soils. Many legumes, gorse included, are able to live in poor soil because they have blue-green algal nodules in their roots which can fix atmospheric nitrogen, so essential for growth. Gorse is a rapid coloniser of open ground, especially in the lowlands, and has been recorded in most, if not all, English counties. Because of its colonising abilities, it was one of sixty species chosen for planting on the sides of motorways in the 1960s. The only parts of Britain where it does not occur are the mountainous areas of northern England and parts of western Scotland and the heavily cultivated fenlands of East Anglia. By contrast, *U. gallii,* the Western Furze, occurs on acid heaths mainly in the west of England, Wales and southern Scotland and is predominant in the lowland acid heaths of southern and western parts of Ireland, where the climate is milder and more oceanic. *U.*

minor, the Dwarf Furze, thrives on the drier heathlands of southern and south-east England, from Dorset to Kent, but is also localised to parts of East Anglia, Nottinghamshire, Lincolnshire and Cumbria.

In the British heathlands, the gorses are part of complex heather-gorse systems. Heather-gorse heaths are called 'oceanic' because they occur in many lowland places where the soils are favourably acid and the land is influenced by relatively warmer oceanic winds. Floristically, heathlands are quite poor. Gorse is usually the abundant or co-dominant species which prevents the growth of many other plants. The different gorse species have different requirements and occur in different parts of Britain because the climate is increasingly oceanic towards the west. Gorse and heather are both extremely inflammable and because of their lowland position are apt to catch fire easily in dry summers. The periodic fires impoverish the flora, reduce the scrub and maintain a fire-climax vegetation of heather and gorse.

15

15. *Dwarf Gorse (Ulex minor) mixed with Ling (Calluna vulgaris) and Dorset Heath (Erica ciliaris).*

However, most heath complexes are not true climaxes. They are associated with man's use of the land for providing grazing and fodder for herbivores, now mainly cattle and sheep but formerly also for goats, horses and even rabbits. The heath and scrub habitat is a transient one between grassland and forest when range management is at a low ebb. If the heaths were totally abandoned they would eventually develop into forests.

HEATHLAND DECLINE AND WILDLIFE

Because of their distribution, the heather-gorse heathlands have probably been part of Britain's countryside heritage for millions of years but we do not know for certain because the only positive historical evidence of gorse has been archaeological. There are neolithic finds from Dorset, iron age finds from Norfolk and Suffolk and Roman deposits from Chester and Ehaside Tarn in Cumbria. From at least the iron age until the eighteenth century, when nearly 40,000 hectares (100,000 acres) of heathland are thought to have existed in Hampshire and Dorset, there has been a steady decline in heathland, mainly through reclamation for agriculture, conifer plantations, urban redevelopment, quarrying and mining. Today in the same areas there are only about 6,000 hectares (15,000 acres). Many are fragmented to less than 0.1 hectare (¼ acre) and very few sites boast more than 100 hectares (250 acres). The picture is much the same for other areas.

Such a decline is a pity because it indicates not a reversion to natural woodland but just a further decline in what is already effectively second-rate countryside. However, heathlands provide good homes for a number of the rarer birds and reptiles. Mixed heather, gorse and bracken heaths often attract the Nightjar *(Caprimulus europaeus),* a species which has largely disappeared from traditional nesting sites. Furthermore, the heaths of the New Forest, Dorset and parts of Sussex comprise almost the total breeding range in Britain for the Dartford Warbler *(Sylvia undata).* A species more at home in the Mediterranean maquis than in English heath, it prefers those places with scattered gorse and seedling trees, like birches, which act as perches. Although an English resident, the Dartford warbler suffers in the cold winters. Gorse provides a thick cover, protecting it from the cold winds, and a rich invertebrate fauna as a winter food supply. Two other southern heathland birds which can be found nesting in the gorse are the Stonechat or Gorse Chat *(Sylvicola torquata),* which likes gorsy sea cliffs, and the Red-backed Shrike *(Lanius collurio).* Many of the popular names given to birds refer to the importance of gorse in their habitat. These include 'Furzeling' for the Dartford Warbler, 'Furze chat' for the Whinchat *(Saxicola rubetira),* 'Gorse hatcher' for the Wheatear *(Oenanthe oenanthe)* and 'Gorse Bird' or 'Gorse Thatcher' for the Linnet *(Acanthis cannabina).*

The six species of British reptiles are found on lowland heaths and gorse-covered coastal sand dunes. Their habitat requirements are different so that each occupies a different niche within the heathland complexes. The Adder hibernates in holes and recesses of various kinds in the dry heaths, whereas the

Grass Snake needs open ponds, dykes or rivers nearby. The Smooth Snake and the rare Sand Lizard occupy dry, open heathland throughout the year although they are much more dependent on the height of the co-dominant heaths than on the gorse. The Common Lizard and the Slow-worm occupy a much wider range of habitats although they prefer the drier heathlands. The southern heaths of Dorset, Hampshire and Surrey are the best British localities for reptiles and in these places all six species can occur on the same site.

It is not only the larger animals which are attracted to the heathlands, but many invertebrates too. Particularly interesting are the moths which have close associations with individual parts of the gorse.

The caterpillars of the Common Headbelle *(Scopopteryx mucronata)* and its relative the July Headbelle *(S. ivridata pilularia)* feast on the leaves. Other species such as *Mirificanna mulinella* and *Brachmia genonella* live off the flowers; *Cydia internana* and *Coleophora albicosta* devour the seeds; *Batia lambdella* favours dead twigs and *Phyllonorycter ulicicolella* eats the bark.

16. *Dwarf Gorse: a close-up of the shoots.*

Economic uses of gorse

Gorse has been of economic importance throughout its history, most particularly in Ireland, where it played a very large part in the rural economy of many areas until relatively recent times. One of its main attributes is that it kindles very easily. It was used as an alternative fuel when wood and peat were in short supply before the development of the coal trade. In the bronze age, when much of the heathland of Sussex, Hampshire and Dorset is thought to have originated through the attempts of early farmers at pastoral management, gorse would have been a very likely source of fuel for smelting furnaces, as well as for domestic fireplaces. As a household fuel, gorse was quite important, especially in the middle ages. Many local records state that villagers could cut gorse growing on the commons. In Ireland its value was so great that the Church levied tithes on it from as early as 1560 until at least the eighteenth century.

Gorse as a fuel has the other advantages of giving out intense heat when burnt and leaving little ash residue. It was used at one time for firing brick, tile and lime kilns, particularly in the south and south-west of England, and for fuelling bakers' ovens, especially in Ireland, with records from as early as 1568. Its use for baking could date back to at least the thirteenth century with the introduction of bakeries to monastery houses and the subsequent arrival of common ovens in the towns. In the seventeenth century the amount of gorse being brought into and stored in Dublin was so great that there were a great many complaints about the hazards of having great stacks of it near the city walls, where they 'doe overtopp the said walles in height'. To ensure an adequate supply of gorse, areas were planted on the farms and close to the kilns. Good examples can still be seen today in Devon and Cornwall (where they were known as 'vuzz brakes') and

also in Wales, Scotland and Ireland. With the development of the coal trade, however, the use of gorse for fuel declined, although it was still used for kindling until recent times. A side-product was a soap substitute made from the ashes mixed with clay.

A second important use of gorse was as fodder for cattle and horses, particularly in winter and when other foodstuffs were in short supply. The leaves are very nutritious, although they can only be grazed when young and tender. Large areas of gorse were cultivated by farmers, especially in Ireland, Scotland and Wales. *Ulex europaeus,* the preferred species, is said to have been introduced to western and northern Wales from Ireland in the eighteenth century for this purpose.

To make the gorse palatable for livestock, it had to be cut and then pounded to crush the hard prickles. The earliest method was to pound the gorse on stone blocks or in tubs, troughs or pits with a variety of mallets, spades or choppers, according to local preference. In the Isle of Man waterwheels were used to move wooden mallets to crush the hard greenery. Later, as the need for more mechanised methods grew, the gorse came to be crushed in various mills (such as cider mills) until early in the nineteenth century, when machines were specifically designed for chopping gorse for fodder. In Scotland, an alternative was the whin bruiser, a reinforced flail, or the more advanced whin mills. Of the latter there were two types, the roller type and the wheel or grindstone type. They basically worked on a pivot system whereby the chopped gorse was crushed by a stone wheel running over it while lying in a circular 'course' or channel that had been reinforced with stones. Gorse was mostly used as fodder in the eighteenth and nineteenth centuries but it is still eaten by rabbits and wild ponies to supplement their diets when grazing is scarce on the heaths and moors.

Gorse has been of value as protective hedging. It is a typical feature of the Irish countryside, having been sown and planted for fencing since the eighteenth century, when acts were passed that required neighbouring landowners and

17. *A gorse bruiser made by Barrett, Exall and Andrews, from the 'Illustrated London News', 1851.*

18. *An Irishman cutting gorse with a sickle and furze fork.*

19. *Common Gorse and hawthorn hedges in Ireland during May.*

tenants to divide their holdings. Examples of this can be seen in Britain today and a particularly attractive setting is in West Sussex where the smock and post mills of 'Jack' and 'Jill' stand by the South Downs Way on Clayton Hill. The best time to visit is Easter, when the gorse is blooming profusely.

There have been many other uses of gorse. It has been woven into hurdles for sheltering cattle, put down as bedding for them and used as a manure, either having been rotted down in the farmyard or spread as ashes after burning with peat. It has been planted as fox coverts in the Midlands and southern England, made into walking sticks and umbrella handles, and used as a foundation for hay and corn stacks in Ireland and as a roofing material on cattle sheds. It has served as a bonding agent in the construction of mud walls and as road foundations.

Gorse has been used medicinally for both man and his animals, but only to a small extent. In the early herbals of Gerard, Parkinson and Culpeper it was said that a decoction of the flowers would help conditions of jaundice, stones or gravel in the kidneys, and obesity. In Ireland the blossoms have been used as a cure for coughs, hoarseness, worms in young children and as a tonic, while the young tops were used to cure hiccoughs, heartburn and swellings. An infusion of the blossoms was given to children as a cure for scarlet fever. Gorse potions also had the reputation of being able to cure a snake bite. Infusions were given to horses as a tonic and as a cure for stomach ailments including worms and botfly, the larvae of which parasitise their stomach lining. Gorse was also used as an insecticide: 'Against fleas, take this same wort, with its seed, sodden; sprinkle it in the house; it killeth the fleas.'

The fragrant blossoms have been used in the flavouring of beverages at least since Tudor times, when Henry VIII is said to have regularly enjoyed a glass of gorse wine. More recently, the Irish have

20

20. *Gorse being mashed on a whinstone.*

used the flowers to flavour their whiskey. Today, blooms are still used for making gorse wine and tea, the blossoms being at their best when collected early in the morning in mid spring, when the weather has been dry and sunny.

In the preparation of cloth, the ash of gorse branches has been used for ridding spun wool of its grease by adding it to the water in which the wool was to be washed, and also as a lye for washing and bleaching linen. The flowers and bark have been used as a dye and still provide a yellow colour used in the manufacture of tartan cloth. A modern use of gorse has been in France in the preparation of men's toiletries. A range called 'Ajonc' (the French for gorse) includes soap, after-shave lotion and eau-de-toilette.

The surprisingly varied uses of gorse, showing man's ability to make use of available local material, are now mostly outdated or very localised. However, their legacy remains in the large tracts of land which welcome the spring after a dreary winter, described by P. W. Izzard: 'the gold ... of the gorse ... the dazzling breadth of the commonland, the fire-fringed cliffs and the flaming hillsides, the burning bushes on the banks by railroad, high-road and byway.'

Customs, folklore and literature

Gorse is a species which has been well known since ancient times but surprisingly it has less folklore and history and fewer customs linked to it than many other plants of similar antiquity. Most folklore is Irish, perhaps because of its far greater importance to the Irish rural economy than any others. However, references to it are scattered throughout English lore and literature, the latter being well covered in V. Rendell's *Wild Flowers in English Literature*.

One of the most popular maxims associated with gorse is 'When gorse is out of fashion, kissing is out of season', taking advantage of the fact that gorse is in bloom most of the year round, with the three species flowering at different times.

In many areas of Ireland gorse was one of the plants used in the May Day celebrations of *lá bealtaine* and 'bringing in the summer'. The sun was thought to rise earlier that day and the witches and fairies were believed to be particularly active, thereby putting at risk the milk and butter which could be 'stolen' or 'bewitched'. The rowan and the hawthorn are the main plants associated with their protection but there are also occasions when gorse was used. 'Furze played a great part in the protection of butter on that day and its preceding night. When the milk was poured into its different bowls, the furze blossom, which is always in bloom just then, was carefully arranged about each container while the bush carefully guarded entrances and exits.' Cattle were also protected by rituals to ward off evil and disease. These often entailed the cattle being forced to walk over or through gorse bonfires or having a burning gorse branch waved under their udders, struck on their backs or thrown in their field.

To protect the home, a 'May bush' was often planted near the house, consisting of a gorse branch in full bloom decorated with trimmings of flowers, ribbons or anything else considered appropriate. Other alternatives were to lay the gorse branches on the windowsills or threshold of the house, hang them over the doorway or place them in the thatch. The length of time they remained there varied from one day to a whole year, up to next May Day, according to local customs. Gorse was also placed over the doorways of the Welsh in Anglesey at this time as protection against the 'mischievous' folk.

Other Irish customs in which gorse played a part include Hunting the Wren on St Stephen's Day and Trundling the Egg at Easter. The former consisted of a group of young men visiting different houses while carrying a decorated branch on to which had been attached a wren that they had caught and killed. On arrival they sang the following song, although the branch used was not necessarily one of gorse:
'The wren! the wren! the king of all birds! St Stephen's Day was caught in the furze.'
Trundling the Egg took place mainly in northern Ireland as part of the Easter festivities and in some areas it still continues. Eggs were hard-boiled and dyed with gorse blossoms. They were then taken up into the hills, and among other games that would take place Trundling the Egg would be foremost. The format varied with the different localities but the principle was that the eggs were thrown or rolled as a competition and then the broken bits were gathered and eaten.

A Yorkshire custom was to sing the chant of the 'Lyke-Wake Dirge' at funerals. It tells of the soul of the dead man arriving for judgement on Whinny-muir. If he had behaved uncharitably, the gorse would prick him to the bone and he would then have to continue his journey to possible hell and purgatory.

'When thou from hence art away past,
Every night and alle,
To Whinny-muir thou com'st at last;
And Christ receive thy saule.

If ever thou gav'st hosen and shoon,
Every night and alle,
Sit thee down and put them on;
And Christ receive thy saule.

If hosen and shoon thou ne'er gav'st nane,
Every night and alle,
The whinnies shall prick thee to the bare bane;
And Christ receive thy saule ...'

Gorse also has more pleasant associations. In the 'language of flowers', a Victorian conceit whereby plants and flowers were given special meanings and posies of sentiments were given to friends, gorse had the attribute of enduring affection. In Ireland, if you wore a sprig of gorse, it protected you from stumbling.

Every year on the last Sunday of June a festival or 'gorse feast' is held in the medieval village of Roquebrune in southern France, when all the children dress up in costumes decorated with gorse blossoms. The ancient village is built halfway down a mountainside overlooking the Mediterranean Sea between Menton and Monaco, the foundations resting on a platform created by a landslide which occurred in the seventh century. The festival celebrates the legend of how the village was saved from sliding into the sea and certain destruction by the presence of three gorse bushes. The legend tells of how, at that time, the young of the village

21. *Linnaeus giving thanks on Putney Heath on seeing the gorse in flower.*

were in danger from Sirens who would attract them down to the sea, where they would then be drowned. A young maiden was climbing up the mountain one day to pray to the Holy Virgin for her fiancé when she was stopped by an old lady who advised her to throw three sticks across the slope of the mountain and escape the influence of the Sirens. The young girl did as suggested and carried on her way, while from the sticks three gorse bushes grew. The Sirens feared that their power over the young people had been diminished and decided to destroy the whole village by making it slide down the mountainside to the sea. However, the gorse bushes arrested the slide and the village came to a halt at the point where it rests today.

A story that inspired much poetry and prose in Victorian times is associated with Linnaeus, the 'Father of Natural History'. Linnaeus had tried to cultivate gorse in his greenhouse in Uppsala in his native Sweden, as the winters there were too cold for it to survive naturally. Oscar Wilde in *De Profundis* tells the story that while on Putney Heath 'Linnaeus fell on his knees and wept for joy when he saw for the first time the long heath of some English upland made yellow with the tawny aromatic blossoms of the English furze...' Linnaeus had, however, seen gorse in flower before, as he had recorded in his travel diary of the previous year, *Iter ad Exteros* (Journey Abroad), that while on the way to Lubeck he had seen that 'The heaths were adorned with gorse with its fine yellow flowers'.

The same story was mentioned in Elizabeth Barrett Browning's poem 'Lessons from the Gorse':

'Mountain gorses, ever golden
Cankered not the whole year long!
Do you teach us to be strong,
Howsoever pricked and holden,
Like your thorny blossoms, and so

23

Trodden on by rain and snow,
Up the hill-side of this life, as bleak as
  where ye grow?

Mountain blossoms, shining blossoms,
Do ye teach us to be glad
When no summer can be had,
Blooming in our inward bosoms?
Ye colour God preserveth still,
Set as lights upon the hill;
Tokens for the wintry earth that beauty
  liveth still.

Mountain gorses, do ye teach us
From that academic chair
Canopied with azure air,
That the wisest word man reaches
Is the humblest he can speak?
Ye who live on mountain peak,
Yet live low along the ground, beside the
  grasses meek!

Mountain gorses, since Linnaeus
Knelt beside you on the sod;
For your beauty, thanking God, —
For your teaching you should see us

Bowing in protestation new!
Whence arisen, — if one or two
Drops be on our cheeks, — O would they
  are not tears but dew.'

Gorse is usually depicted in literature as a welcome herald of the spring with its golden blooms brightening up the countryside after winter or as part of the autumn tapestry of the moors, mixing its colours with the soft purples of the heather. It provides a haven for the wildlife associated with it. It has always been very much a part of the English countryside and that association is summed up by P. Izzard in *Homeland:* 'The splendour of our loved homeland gorses in glowing sunlight is something to see ever with new joy and wonderment, and to still see with that inward eye long after the bloom is dimmed, carrying the vision wherever we may roam — a picture of England as dear as the primrose lane and the bluebell wood, the purple moor, the poppied cornfield and the old-world garden.'

Further reading

Blunt, W. *The Compleat Naturalist; A Life of Linnaeus.* Collins, 1971.
Clapham, A. R., Tutin, T. G., and Warburg, E. F. *Flora of the British Isles.* Cambridge University Press, 1962.
Fairhurst, A., and Soothill, E. *A Blandford Guide to Trees of the British Countryside.* Blandford, 1981.
Grigson, G. *The Englishman's Flora.* Paladin, 1975.
Grinsberg, S. and E. *The Perched Villages of the Alpes Maritimes.* Edisod La Calade, Aix-en-Provence, 1983.
Heinzel, H., Fitter, R., and Parslow, J. *The Birds of Britain and Europe.* Collins, 1972.
Holden, E. *The Country Diary of an Edwardian Lady.* Michael Joseph, Webb and Bower, 1977.
Perring, F. H., and Walters, S. M. *Atlas of the British Flora.* BSBI and EP Publishing, second edition 1976.
Rendell, V. *Wild Flowers in Literature.* George Allen and Unwin Ltd, 1934.
Ritchie, J. 'Whin bruisers and whin-mills'. *Scottish Journal of Agriculture* 13 (1930), 390-8.
Ross-Craig, S. *Drawings of British Plants. VII — Leguminosae.* Bell and Sons, 1954.
Tansley, A. *Britain's Green Mantle.* George Allen and Unwin Ltd, second edition 1968.
Tutin, T. G., Heywood, V. H., Burges, N. A., Moore, D. M., Valentine, D. H., Walters, S. M. and Webb, D. A. (editors). *Flora Europaea* (volume 2). Cambridge University Press, 1968.

ACKNOWLEDGEMENTS
We would like to thank Mr Miki Slingsby for photographing and printing the line drawings and Mr Roy Vickery of the British Museum (Natural History) for pointing us in the right directions in matters of folklore. Illustrations are acknowledged to: Heather Angel of Biofotos, cover and figs. 5, 10, 15, 19; Messrs Bell and Sons, for permission to reproduce figs. 1, 2, 4; Miss Gina Douglas of the Linnean Society library, for permission to reproduce fig. 21; Dr F. H. Perring and BSBI and EP Publishing, for permission to reproduce the maps in figs. 12, 13, 14; Dr M. Proctor, figs. 7, 8, 9; the Ulster Folk and Transport Museum, figs. 18, 20.